My Fur Baby

Name: _____

Published by Hinkler Books Pty Ltd
45–55 Fairchild Street
Heatherton Victoria 3202 Australia
www.hinkler.com

hinkler

Authors: Zoe Antony and Sam Kiley
Cover design: Hinkler Design Studio
Internal design: Lisa Howard
Prepress: Splitting Image

ISBN: 978 1 4889 3430 8

Printed and bound in China

CONTENTS

MY PURRFECT PET'S PROFILE

My perfect new name

....

Other potential names

....

....

....

Why my name was chosen

....

....

....

My breed

....

Known family or rescue origin

....

Age when I became part of the family

....

The camera loves me!

The colour of my eyes

....

What is my fur like?
(long/short/none)

....

The colour of my fur

....

This is a lock of my fur

My birthday

....

My star sign

....

My personality
(sum me up in 5 words!)

....

....

....

....

....

Introverted or extroverted?

....

When I'm happy, I...

....

....

....

....

....

....

When I'm cranky, I...

....

....

....

....

....

*The smallest feline
is a masterpiece.*
LEONARDO DA VINCI

5

IMPORTANT INFORMATION ABOUT ME

Microchip number

....

Council registration number

....

Council registration records/renewals

....

....

....

....

....

....

Allergies

....

....

....

Emergency contacts
(family and friend connections)

....

....

....

....

....

....

Remember:
- use non-toxic ink
- be gentle with your cat's paw
- immediately wash off the ink with warm, cat-friendly, soapy water

My first paw print

MY PUBLIC PROFILE

Our Instagram/Facebook/
Twitter account/s

....

....

....

....

How many followers I have

....

My picture
that has the
most likes

A cat has absolute emotional
honesty: human beings, for
one reason or another, may hide
their feelings, but a cat does not.

ERNEST HEMINGWAY

My profile pics

MY FAMILY AND FRIENDS

My owner

....

....

....

Other family members

....

....

....

My family and friends

Our first home

....

....

....

Home, sweet home

My other pet brothers or sisters

....

....

....

....

Other people and pets I'm friends with

....

....

....

....

Before a cat will condescend
To treat you as a trusted friend,
Some little token of esteem
Is needed, like a dish of cream.
T.S. ELIOT

My First Days

We first met on (date)

....

At this location

....

....

....

What was special about me

....

....

....

....

....

My first reaction to my new home

....

....

....

....

....

I'm finally here!

After a couple of hours, I...

....

....

....

....

....

....

At the end of my first week, I...

....

....

....

....

....

....

What happened on my first night

....

....

....

....

....

....

....

One small cat changes
coming home to an empty
house to coming home.

PAM BROWN

The most memorable moment
from our first week!

OUR FIRSTS

My first meal

....

....

Yum!

My first catnap

....

....

Zzzz!

My first use of the litterbox

....

....

So proud!

First time I fell asleep on my owner

....

....

Aww!

12

First time I meowed

....

....

First time I purred

....

....

First time I rubbed against my owner's leg and face

....

....

....

....

Puuurrrrr

My first trip to the vet

....

....

....

My first journey outside

....

....

....

....

My first journey in the car or on public transport

....

....

....

....

....

DID YOU KNOW?

Cats can pick up on your tone of voice, so sweet-talking your cat has more of an impact than you think!

MY FAVOURITE THINGS

My favourite foods

....
....
....
....

My favourite places to be stroked

Circle on the diagram

My favourite place to sleep

....
....

Here's me busy catnapping

My favourite toys

....

....

Here's me with my toy babies

My favourite games

....

....

Here's me being cheeky

My favourite places to hide

....

....

....

Cats are connoisseurs of comfort.
JAMES HERRIOT

Here's me being sneaky

OUR TYPICAL DAY

This is our typical day

....

....

....

....

....

....

....

This morning we woke up at .... o'clock

Ready for some breakfast!

This is where I take a nap

We play together at.............. o'clock

We have dinner at.............. o'clock

We go to bed at.............. o'clock

Activity time!

Dinner time!

Time for bed

DID YOU KNOW?
When a household cat died in ancient Egypt, its owners showed their grief by shaving off their own eyebrows.

OUR FIRST CATAVERSARY!

What we did to celebrate our cataversary

....
....
....
....
....
....

Our best moment from the past year

....
....
....
....
....
....

What we learnt in the past year

....
....
....
....
....

Developments and highlights from the past year

....
....
....
....
....
....
....
....
....
....
....
....
....
....
....
....
....
....
....
....
....
....
....
....

Celebrating our first cataversary together

DID YOU KNOW?

Collectively, all the kittens in the world yawn about 200 million times per hour.

GETTING UP TO MISCHIEF

Here's me being naughty in style!

Examples could include:

- Chewing or scratching things (or people) I shouldn't

- Willfully knocking things off high shelves

- Performing daring balancing and acrobatic acts

- Being fussy with food or swatting it over

Cats can work out mathematically the exact place to sit that will cause most inconvenience.

PAM BROWN

OUR BIG ADVENTURES!

Our notable travels, outings and adventures include

....
....
....
....
....

....
....
....
....
....
....

....
....
....
....
....

....

....

....

....

....

                           ....

                           ....

                           ....

                           ....

                           ....

....

....

....

....

....

DID YOU KNOW?

A group of kittens is called a 'kindle', while a group of adult cats are called a 'clowder' or a 'glaring'.

23

FELINE FEELINGS

I am a complex cat.

This is me when I am...

Sad

Happy

Grumpy

Playful

Angry

Excited

THIRD CATAVERSARY

What we did to celebrate our cataversary

....
....
....
....
....

Our best moment from the past two years

....
....
....
....
....

What we learnt in the past two years

....
....
....
....
....

Our highlights from the past two years

....
....
....
....
....
....
....
....
....
....
....
....
....
....
....
....
....
....
....
....
....
....

Celebrating our third cataversary together

DID YOU KNOW?
If your cat's eyes are closed, it's not necessarily because it's tired; it can also mean that your cat is happy or pleased.

CATUMES

Two of my favourite catumes or catssessories

Two of my least favourite catumes or catssessories

DID YOU KNOW?
A female cat is called a 'queen' or a 'molly' and a male cat a 'tomcat' – 'tom' for short.

POSES AND HIDEY HOLES

My strange sleeping poses

My eccentric sitting pose

Cats sleep anywhere,
any table, any chair,

Top of piano, window-ledge,
in the middle, on the edge.

Open drawer, empty shoe,
anybody's lap will do,

Fitted in a cardboard box,
in the cupboard with your frocks.

Anywhere! They don't care!
Cats sleep anywhere.

ELEANOR FARJEON

Peculiar places I like to sit

An odd place I like to hide

FIFTH CATAVERSARY

What we did to celebrate our cataversary

....
....
....
....
....

Our best moment from the past two years

....
....
....
....
....

What we learnt in the past two years

....
....
....
....

Celebrating our fifth cataversary together

DID YOU KNOW?
Cats conserve energy by sleeping for an average of 13 to 14 hours a day.

Our highlights from the past two years

....
....
....
....
....
....
....
....
....
....
....
....
....
....
....
....
....
....
....
....
....
....
....

MY GROWN-UP KITTY

How my tastes have changed over the years

....
....
....
....
....
....
....
....
....
....
....
....
....
....
....
....
....
....
....

So mature!

My favourite pastime is

....

....

....

....

....

....

How my personality has changed

....

....

....

....

....

....

DID YOU KNOW?
Cats have the cognitive ability to sense a human's feelings and overall mood. When their owner smiles, cats are more likely to demonstrate happy and affectionate behaviour, like purring or sitting on their owner's lap.

Special snaps!

LET'S CELEBRATE!

These are some kitty highlights of special events

....

....

....

....

....

....

....

....

....

....

....

....

....

....

....

....

....

....

....

This is how we celebrated these special occasions

....
....
....
....
....
....
....
....
....
....
....
....
....
....
....
....
....
....
....
....
....
....

DID YOU KNOW?
Cats need only about one-sixth of the light humans need to function in the dark.

LET'S CELEBRATE MORE!

This is how we celebrate special occasions

....
....
....
....
....
....

....
....
....
....
....
....

....
....
....
....
....

If there were to be a universal sound depicting peace, I would surely vote for the purr.
BARBARA L. DIAMOND

MY GROWTH

Date	Age	Length	Height	Weight

My evolution!

TOP TIP!

For best health, domestic cats should weigh about 4.5 kilograms (10 pounds), though that can vary by breed and frame. A Siamese cat may weigh as few as just over 2 kilos (5 pounds), while a Maine Coon can be over 10 kilos (25 pounds) and healthy. Ideally a cat should have an hourglass figure when you look at them from above and you should be able to feel their ribs.

VACCINATIONS AND TREATMENTS

This should include core vaccinations like feline infectious enteritus, and non-core vaccines, like feline respiratory disease (cat flu).

Vaccination Type	Due By	Appointment On

Treatment (worming, flea control, etc.)	Due By	Medications

TOP TIP!

Give your cat their pill in their favourite treat, and in a portion of this food that is small and soft enough so that they don't chew it but just lick and swallow the piece whole. Give a pill-free treat, followed by the treat with the pill, followed by another pill-free treat. Since cats are extremely clever, it's wise to change up the order of which treat the pill will be in each time you need to repeat this process.

VISITS TO THE VET

Date	Reason	Treatment	Notes

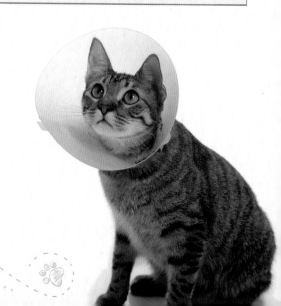

Date	Reason	Treatment	Notes

TOP TIP!

It's not surprising that most cats learn to fear the cat carrier. It is usually associated with an unpleasant trip in a car that ends up at a vet. You can help get your cat more comfortable by making positive associations with the carrier. For example, leaving the carrier out days before you need to use it, let them explore it and even feed them inside it. Using a towel your cat has slept on will also help to make the carrier more familiar and comforting.

THE PAWFECT TEAM

Me and you together (furever!)

Aaaaaawwwww!

What greater gift than the love of a cat?
CHARLES DICKENS

Cat Milestone Cards

Use these cards to mark important or adorable moments in your fur baby's life. Simply cut out the card you want to use, place it beside your cat and take a photo of the memorable moment! You can use some of these cards multiple times, especially the cataversary card, which has room to write what cataversary you're celebrating.

My First Day At Home

First Night In My Bed

Our _____ Cataversary

My First Meal

IT'S PLAYTIME!

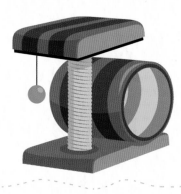

IT'S GOOD TO BE BAD

SLEEPING? I'M BUSY PLOTTING

BEING 100% ADORABLE